HORRIBLE SCIENCE
TEACHERS' RESOURCES

PLANTS

Nick Arnold • Tony De Saulles
additional material David Tomlinson

AUTHOR
Nick Arnold

ILLUSTRATIONS
Tony De Saulles

ADDITIONAL MATERIAL
David Tomlinson

EDITOR
Wendy Tse

ASSISTANT EDITOR
Charlotte Ronalds

SERIES DESIGNER
Joy Monkhouse

DESIGNER
Helen Taylor
Erik Ivens

This book contains extracts from *Vicious Veg*, *Suffering Scientists* and *The Awfully Big Quiz Book* in the Horrible Science series. Text © 1998, 2000, 2000, Nick Arnold. Illustrations © 1998, 2000, 2000, Tony De Saulles. First published by Scholastic Children's Books. Additional text © 2005, David Tomlinson.

Designed using Adobe InDesign

Published by Scholastic Ltd
Villiers House
Clarendon Avenue
Leamington Spa
Warwickshire
CV32 5PR

www.scholastic.co.uk

Printed by Bell & Bain Ltd, Glasgow

2 3 4 5 6 7 8 9   5 6 7 8 9 0 1 2 3 4

...AND HOW LONG HAS THIS APPLE PIP BEEN STUCK BETWEEN YOUR TEETH, MR SMITH?

British Library Cataloguing-in-Publication Data
A catalogue record for this book is available from the British Library.

ISBN 0-439-97184-5
ISBN 978-0439-97184-3
The right of David Tomlinson to be identified as the Author of additional text of this Work has been asserted by him in accordance with the Copyright, Designs and Patents Act 1988.

TEACHERS' NOTES

Horrible Science: Teachers' Resources – Plants is inspired by the Horrible Science book *Vicious Veg*. Each photocopiable page takes a weird and wonderful excerpt from the original, as well as material from *Suffering Scientists* and *The Awfully Big Quiz Book*, and expands on it to create a class-based teaching activity, fulfilling both National Curriculum and QCA objectives. The activities can be used individually or in a series as part of your scheme of work.

   With an emphasis on research, experimentation and interpreting results, the activities will appeal to anyone even remotely curious about the Horrible world around us!

PART 1:
INTRODUCING VEGETATION

Page 11: Vicious vegetation!
Learning objective
To make careful observations of plants and their surroundings.
To record and interpret observations.

Start this introductory session by asking your class to describe a local park or green part of the playground. Encourage them to give details about what they might expect to see growing there. Use photocopiable page 11 to introduce the idea that although we may think of plants as simply 'being there' they are eating, drinking, growing, breeding and fighting among themselves. Divide your class into groups for a mini field trip and ask each group to measure a square metre in the green area, marking it out with string and pegs. Encourage the children to get close up and use magnifying glasses to look at their 'patch'. Highlight any creatures that live in the square, stressing their coexistence with plants. Ask your class to draw everything that they see in the square as a map. Then join the maps together like patchwork in class to recreate the 'outside', complete with labels, for a display that you can add to as your lessons progress.
SAFETY NOTE! Risk assessment may be necessary. Warn the children not to touch any litter or 'muck'. Magnifying glasses should not be kept on the same spot of grass on a sunny day, as there is a danger of starting an unplanned study of fire!

Page 12: Poisonous plants!
Learning objective
To use and present appropriate methods of research effectively.

Use the Horrible Health Warning on photocopiable page 12 to introduce the concept that it is not safe for humans to eat certain plants and vegetables. Encourage the children to research exactly which plants humans should avoid, stressing that different plants are harmful to different creatures. Ramblers organisations and countryside charities are good sources of information. Use this research as the basis for posters for a class display. This is also a good opportunity to talk about how to handle plants safely and without damaging them, establishing why picking flowers in the wild can damage a habitat.

Page 13: Disgusting dissection
Learning objective
To use simple apparatus to observe.
To record observations.

Begin this session by asking your class to describe some plants. Explain that it can be argued that the most interesting parts of the plant are hidden from view. Introduce the word 'dissection': this is what scientists do when they need to look 'inside' something. Give each child or pair of children a leaf from a plant; succulents are best for this observation, or sugar snap pea pods if you don't want to butcher a prize succulent. Use scissors to cut the subject and ask the children to draw what they see. They will not see much detail even with a magnifying glass, but they will notice that there is 'goo' and layers, and relate this to the diagrams on the photocopiable.

Page 14: Wonder Veg World!
Learning objective
To make careful observations of plants and their surroundings.
To record and interpret observations.

Invite your class to bring in vegetables from home, including any unusual examples. Use photocopiable page 14 to record observations, encouraging the children to feel and smell the vegetables as well as to examine and measure them. Share observations and use the photocopiable sheet as the basis for a display. **SAFETY NOTE!** Agree a class rule of not eating the examples because unwashed food can carry germs.

Page 15: Plants: the secret fact file
Learning objective
Plants need healthy roots, leaves and stems to live. Humans use plants and some are grown for this purpose.

Use photocopiable page 15 as the basis for a session in which you encourage your class to share the names of as many different plants as they can, as well as describing them and how humans may use them. Pictures from cooking and gardening magazines are useful for cutting up to add to the fact files, and encourage the class to divide the plants into groups based on what we do and do not eat, as well as adding their own criteria.

Page 16: Attack of the killer plants!
Learning objective
To use prediction and hypothesis to determine an outcome.
Plants need healthy roots, leaves and stems to live.

Recap any work your class may have done on what plants need in order to live. Focus on the need for light. Explain that plants fight each other for access to light above the ground and their roots fight for water and minerals in the soil. Use the activity to illustrate this concept, encouraging the children to take on the role of the plant afterwards to make a dramatic confession in a class court.
Answer: c) The tendril is making ready to coil around the pencil. It thinks the pencil is another plant stalk. Within a few hours the centre of the tendril will coil like a telephone flex and pull the entire plant towards the pencil.

Page 17: Frightful fruity facts
Learning objective
To know the names of the parts of flowering plants.

Bring in as many examples of the foods shown on the sheet as possible and explain that you are setting a sorting challenge. Ask your class to work in groups and to share their sorting solutions, explaining their reasons. As an extension, play a game of 'Call my Bluff'. Two groups use their own examples to argue the cases for an object being fruit or vegetable and a third group decides who is right and explains why.
Answers:
Fruits: 1, 2, 3, 4. According to scientists all nuts are fruits. Of course, if you were cruel you might say that some scientists are nuts.
Not fruits: 5 A pineapple forms from several parts of a large number of flowers. This means that, scientifically speaking, a pineapple is not a fruit because it doesn't develop from a single ovary.
6 Strawberries also form from several parts of the flower. The fruits are actually the tiny pips on the sides of the strawberry.
7 Rhubarb is the cooked stalk of the rhubarb plant so it's nothing to do with fruits.

Page 18: Fantastic foods
Learning objective
Some plants can be used as food and that some plants are bred especially for this purpose.
Food chains begin with plants.

Bring in a number of different foods and ask the children to trace the origins of each back to a plant. Include some two- or three-stage examples, such as instant noodles in a pot – a highly processed food with natural origins (noodles are made from flour ground from a plant, the soya bits are the by-product of a plant, and so on) – or cheese (milk coming from cows who have eaten grass) as well as bread, peas, cake and so on. Encourage the children to think of examples of their own and to link this to any work on food chains that you may have done previously. Use photocopiable page 18 to focus your class on recording their discoveries.

===== PART 2: =====
BREEDING PLANTS

Page 19: Pesky pollen 1
Learning objective
Plants reproduce.
Insects pollinate some flowers.
To know the names of the parts of flowering plants.

Use the exotic examples of pollination on photocopiable page 19 to introduce the important role that insects can play in helping plants breed. Link this to examples the children may already have observed (such as bees buzzing around flowers in summer). Use felt balls and Velcro or sticky tape to simulate how the insect carries pollen from one plant to another. Tell the children to look closely at some flowers in groups, asking them where they think the pollen may be. Good examples are daffodils, chrysanthemums and snapdragons, depending on the time of year. Compare the finished drawings, asking the children to hypothesise what might happen next in the plants' breeding process.

Page 20: Pesky pollen 2
Learning objective
Plants reproduce.
Insects pollinate some flowers.
To know the names of the parts of flowering plants.

Start by recapping any observations that your class may have made about pollen and the process of pollination. Discuss the dreaded 'Pollen count' and how it affects people with hay fever. Explain that the children will be taking the part of the insect in this activity by removing the pollen gently from a flower. Follow the instructions on photocopiable page 20 and encourage the children to look closely at what they see, transferring the pollen from one flower to another. Use the strip cartoon boxes on the photocopiable sheet to focus the children on the complete process, introducing the ideas of male and female parts of a flower.
Answer: c) The yellow stuff is pollen (that's the dusty stuff made by flowers that makes you sneeze). To breed plants you simply put it on the stigmas of another plant of the same type. The pollen grows a tube in the second plant and seeds form.

Page 21: Starting seeds
Learning objective
Plants reproduce.
Insects pollinate some flowers.
To know the names of the parts of flowering plants.
Seeds germinate to start new plants.

Recap the pollination process and explain that the next stage is the formation of the seed. Ask the children to name examples of seeds that they have

seen. A sunflower head is a great starting point as the seeds are so evident. Include foods in this discussion and use real examples of those featured on photocopiable page 21. Divide your class into groups, asking them where they think the seeds are hidden in the foods. Cut the foods in front of the children, asking them to draw and compare sizes, shapes, texture, colour, weight and smell. Encourage the children to record their observations accurately in the seed gallery.

Page 22: Seed secrets
Learning objective
Plants reproduce.
Seeds germinate to start new plants.
To consider conditions that might affect germination.

Recap any work you have done observing and comparing the outsides of seeds. Tell your class that now you are going to look inside the bean. Using a broad bean as an example, explain that the seed is a self-contained plant kit and that in the right conditions we can help it grow. Cut open the bean and encourage the children to work in groups to record what they see. Ask them to predict what the bean seed needs in order to grow and how that growth will start. Introduce the word 'germination' and ask the groups to discuss their predictions of how the bean will grow. Give each group a transparent pot or jar with cotton wool, water and a bean seed. Keep it a sunny spot and regularly water (but don't drown) the seed. Record the germination process and compare it to the original predictions.

Page 23: Ripe or revolting?
Learning objective
Plants reproduce.
Seeds germinate to start new plants.
To consider conditions that might affect germination.

This activity is useful for introducing seed dispersal to the concept of plant breeding. Use the examples on photocopiable page 23 to focus the children on the different forms that seeds can take. Explain that seeds from plants such as tomatoes and sunflowers can be eaten by animals and humans; other seeds, such as avocado, are not edible. Sugar snap peas are essentially normal peas picked before being completely ready to seed. Warn the children against eating fruits and seeds straight from the garden, as some of them may be poisonous. Talk about animals being useful seed dispersal units and humans being less useful (we dispose of edible seeds down the toilet whereas animals obligingly get rid of the seed somewhere it has a chance of growing). Use ripe and unripe examples of the foods to illustrate the concept that plants need their seeds to be dispersed at a particular time or season.

Page 24: What's inside?
Learning objective
Scientific investigation.
To predict possible results and outcomes.

Use photocopiable page 24 to look at different types of fruit, asking the children to predict what they may find inside. This activity is particularly useful for less able children or as reinforcement when used with photocopiable page 23. Use the peach as a clear example of skin, flesh and seed, asking the children to use these labels on the other examples, comparing texture, smell, size and colour.

Page 25: Foul fertilisers
Learning objective
To consider the conditions required for successful growth.

Introduce the idea that plants draw minerals as well as water from the earth through their roots. Encourage the children to share any knowledge they have about biodegradable materials or food rotting and how it changes texture and smell. Ask if any of them have a compost bin at home. Apply this to photocopiable page 25, adding further examples of useful fertilisers.

Page 26: Poo corner
Learning objective
To consider the conditions required for successful growth.
To present information successfully.

After introducing the concept that poo is not all bad, recap any work your class may have done on seed dispersal. Not only does poo assist this process but it also contains nutrients that animals do not need or cannot use up in one go. Encourage the children to think of poo as a brand-new product and to think

of advertisements to market it. Share the finished examples and extend into television-style adverts.

PART 3:
NASTY PLANTS AND BUG-EATING MONSTERS

Page 27: Victims of the Venus flytrap!
Learning objective
Different plants are found in different places.
To observe a range of different plants.

If you have access to a Venus flytrap, use it to show the children a different sort of plant than they may be used to. Discourage them from poking it to make it snap as this will use up a lot of the plant's energy and kill it unless there is a juicy fly attached. Talk through the process together, using photocopiable page 27 as the basis for a role-play. Use members of your class to link together to form the trap and others to form the fly. Encourage the children to swap roles and to record their feelings, complete with gore.

Page 28: Unusual suspects
Learning objective
Different plants are found in different places.
To observe a range of different plants.
To record observations.

The children will need to see a range of plants, including a cactus. Some of the plants could be viewed outside the classroom. This activity is useful either to start close observations at the beginning of this topic or to encourage a closer look at plants the children have grown themselves over a period of time. Use the finished posters for a display or presentation.

Pages 29 & 30: Fiendish flowers 1 & 2
Learning objective
Different plants are found in different places.
To know the names of the parts of flowering plants.
To observe a range of different plants.
To record observations.

Use photocopiable pages 29 and 30 to record predictions and observations when looking at the inside of a flower and identifying its different parts. Start by introducing your class to a collection of flowers of different sorts and ask them to describe what they see. Use photocopiable page 29 to recap any work you may have done on pollination and record what the children perceive to be contained inside a flower. Divide your class into groups, asking them to look carefully and peel away the petals so they can see more clearly. Then cut the ovary (with some flowers it may be possible to cut the stamen in half too, although with most this would require micro-surgery). Record the observations on photocopiable page 30, using the labels from the diagram. Compare with predictions from photocopiable page 29.

Pages 31 & 32: Brutal bug-eaters 1 & 2
Learning objective
To observe a range of different plants.
To record observations.
To apply scientific knowledge.

Use photocopiable page 31 to introduce the idea that some plants are designed to eat living creatures, referring to the Venus flytrap (see photocopiable page 27) if appropriate. Ask the children to work in pairs, one acting as the bug-eating plant, the other as prey, and to describe how they work. Challenge your class to think of ideas for their own design, laying down the basic concepts that the plants attract specific creatures (easily digestible bugs) using sneaky tactics. Use photocopiable page 32 for the finished designs and encourage the botanists in your class to give a mini lecture about their new 'discovery'. Extend this activity by making models of the plants for a Freaky Flower Show display.

Page 33: Powerful plants
Learning objective
To research using appropriate materials.

Talk to the children about medicines that they may have had to use (such as cough syrup and aspirin), re-iterating that under no circumstances should they take these things unsupervised. Explain that many of the medicines we take today are derived from plants. For example, cough syrups originally contained rose hips to sooth the throat; cooling mint and menthol oils come from herbs; dock leaves soothe nettle stings as they contain a mild antiseptic. Use photocopiable

page 33 as the starting point to look at how plants can have powerful and useful properties. Encourage your class to research and add their own examples over a period of weeks.

Page 34: Foul fungi
Learning objective
Food chains start with a plant.
To observe and draw conclusions based on observations.

Talk to the children about toadstools in traditional stories and the warnings we associate with them, in order to impress upon the children that eating wild fungi can be fatal. Use photocopiable page 34 to encourage the children to give their own examples and to predict what they think will happen to the food in the activity. You can expand this to include different foodstuffs, comparing the different types of fungi that grow on different foods.
SAFETY NOTE! Ensure that the children do not handle the fungi.
Answer: c) Probably. Fungi grow from spores and they're everywhere. So there were probably a few spores in the air that went into the bag. Throw the bag away unopened – you don't want your fungi to invade your packed lunch, do you?

Page 35: Fungi facts
Learning objective
Plants can provide food for us and some are grown for this purpose.
To observe and draw conclusions based on observations.

Recap all safety warnings regarding eating fungi (see the activity above), and use photocopiable page 35 to focus the children on a type of fungi that we can eat safely: mushrooms. Encourage the children to look closely at both the outside and inside and to record their observations. Oyster mushrooms are largest and handy for younger children although button mushrooms are more useful for looking at the stalks. Compare this to any work you may have done

WHEN WE GET BACK I'M HAVING BACON, EGGS, TOMATOES, AND . . .   MUSHROOMS?

about other types of fungi (see photocopiable page 34).

PART 4:

PHOTOSYNTHESIS AND TRANSPIRATION

Page 36: Fab photosynthesis 1
Learning objective
Plants can make their own food.

Introduce this concept by asking the children to think of the food groups that they need in order to stay alive. Explain that plants can feed themselves and we call this process 'photosynthesis'. Use photocopiable page 36 to explain the first stage of this process: when plants take in sunlight and carbon dioxide through their leaves. This process is the opposite to what humans do. Link the activity to any work your class may have done regarding humans breathing in oxygen and breathing out carbon dioxide.

Page 37: Fab photosynthesis 2 – Rambling roots
Learning objective
Plants can make their own food.
Water is taken in through the roots.

Use this activity to take the children to the next stage of photosynthesis: roots taking in water and minerals. Use the comparison activity as an assessment opportunity, focusing on the children's descriptive as well as written skills. Recap any work on fair testing and explain that scientists design experiments for a purpose. Focus your class on why this experiment could be considered 'fair' and what it can prove, before carrying it out.

Page 38: Fab photosynthesis 3 – Simply starch
Learning objective
Plants can make their own food.
Plants need light for healthy growth.
Plants need healthy roots, leaves and stems to grow well.

Link the foods that plants make to the foods that we eat, explaining that humans also eat sugar and starches. Use the leaf-covering experiment to explain to the children that chlorophyll plays an important part in photosynthesis. For the Simply Starch test just follow these instructions:
1 Boil an ordinary uncovered leaf for 20 seconds and put it in a solution of methylated spirit (70%) and water (30%).
2 Wash the leaf and ask a volunteer to add a few drops of iodine. Black colouring indicates the presence of starch, which shows that photosynthesis has occurred.
3 Repeat with the leaf that you covered up. This will show a different result, as photosynthesis has not taken place because it has had no access to light.

Page 39: Terrific transpiration
Learning objective
Plants need healthy roots, leaves and stems to grow well.
Plants can make their own food.
Water is taken in through the roots.

Use the explanation on photocopiable page 39 as the starting point to see how transpiration is a vital part of photosynthesis. Use the photocopiable sheet to focus the children on predicting sensible outcomes, encouraging them to take 'risks'. Use the predictions and the resulting cartoons for a display, highlighting the usefulness of prediction in science.
Answer: c) These tiny drops of water have been lost from the leaves by transpiration.

PART 5:

LEAVES AND STEMS

Page 40: Luscious leaves
Learning objective
Plants need healthy roots, leaves and stems to grow well.
Plants can make their own food.
Water is taken in through the roots.

Compare leaves from a number of plants in your classroom, looking at colour, shape, measurements and so on. It is good to include examples from plants the children may have been growing in other activities. Urge the children to bring in leaves from home and to group them. Use the leaf-rubbing activity on photocopiable page 40 to encourage the children to look closely at leaf surfaces and to understand what the veins are used for. Use the rubbings for an annotated class display or class Book of Luscious Leaves.

Page 41: Amazing leaf facts
Learning objective
Plants need healthy roots, leaves and stems to grow well.

Plants can make their own food.

Water is taken in through the roots.

Use photocopiable page 41 to encourage your class to research and present their findings clearly for a scientific audience. Focus on the amazing facts, encouraging the children to decide which leaves they would like to know more about. Ask the children to make their own large-sized versions of the leaves and to present them in a class Leaf-a-thon presentation or in the class Book of Luscious Leaves.

Page 42: Stunning stems
Learning objective
Plants need healthy roots, leaves and stems to grow well.

To observe and present observations.

To predict likely outcomes and drawing conclusions from results.

Start this session by splitting a stem of celery to show the inside of a stem and ask the children what they think its job is. Compare other stems, focusing on the carnation. Use the results of the activity on photocopiable page 42 to illustrate the sucking power of a stem and link this to work on photosynthesis to explain why water is so important to plants.

PART 6:

QUIZ AND ASSESSMENT

Page 43: Vital vegetables quiz
Learning objective
To research for scientific purpose.

To draw conclusions based on evidence.

Use this card-based activity as a small-scale assessment when looking at scientific investigative skills. Encourage the children to use books and the internet to find out what the priceless plant product plants look like in order to draw them. Ask the children to find and draw more examples of useful plants.

Answers:

1 b) In Brazil sugar cane is made into alcohol and this is used as a fuel for cars. People buy it from pumps at garages alongside the more traditional petrol pumps.

2 g) In Northern England, in the nineteenth century, people wove stinging nettle stems into tablecloths.

3 f) Laminaria (lam-in-ar-re-a) seaweed feels dry and brittle in dry weather but as rain draws near and the air grows moist, the seaweed takes in water and feels sticky.

4 c) Spaghetti is made out of pasta, which is made from semolina. Yes, this is the same paste-like sludge that is served up as a school dinner pudding. And semolina is made from ground-up grains of wheat.

5 d) Lichens were used to make traditional dyes. A typical recipe involved leaving the dye to rot in a mix of stale pee and a chemical called slaked lime. Are you dying to make it?

6 h) Native South Americans use bixa seeds to make groovy orange hair colour. The juice also keeps mosquitoes away.

7 a) The cotton in your socks is made from hairs that help to disperse the seeds of the cotton plants that are inside their seed pods. The hairs are spun using machines to make the cloth.

8 e) Wellington boots are traditionally made from rubber. Rubber is made from the congealed juice, or latex, that oozes from the rubber tree when you cut its bark. Today a lot of rubber is made in factories using artificial chemicals.

9 i) Yes, you probably knew this one. This book is made from trees. That's where paper comes from. The wood is ground into a pulpy mass of tiny bits called fibres and dissolved using chemicals. Further chemical treatment follows including adding glue to stick the fibres together. This disgusting goo is then pressed and dried and cut to size.

Pages 44 & 45: Jungle of Death quiz 1 & 2
Learning objective
To present ideas clearly.

To draw conclusions based on evidence.

Use this activity as a fun reward for good work. Encourage your children to add their own revolting research!

Answers:

1 b) If you were an Amazon water lily you'd do this to water snails. Spikes are a good way to beat off hungry animals. Tropical screw pines have sword-shaped leaves. The barbs on the leaves mean that any creature that gets too close gets skewered. Even ordinary grass has tiny blades made from a chemical called silica. That's why careless humans sometimes cut themselves on grass.

2 c) Rose bushes defend themselves in this way. The wasps scoop up the caterpillars and take them back to their nest. There the caterpillars are torn apart and fed to the wasp grubs as a tasty tea-time treat. That'll teach them.

3 a) Ants are ideal. The South American ant plant actually provides a cosy little chamber inside its stem for the ants to live in. The plant eats the ants' droppings and the ants kill any insect that comes near. So everyone's happy – except the insects that get killed.

4 c) Stinging nettles do this. Their leaves are covered in tiny hairs. If the hairs are touched poison pours out. A rabbit's nose is very sensitive and rather than risk a sting the bunnies avoid the nettle. In fact, dead nettles (which don't really have a sting) keep the bunnies at bay and avoid getting eaten because they look like stinging nettles. It's a vicious disguise.

5 b) You have to be a viciously cunning oak tree to make this work. The bugs never know when there'll be leaves to eat. If the bugs hatch out too soon they'll starve and if they arrive too late the oak leaves will have had time to make poisons to defend themselves. (So there's half a point for **c)**.)

6 a) It's a vicious trick. High-flying ladybirds can spot the aphids on the outer leaves and chew them up for supper. And serves 'em right!

7 c) This is typically vicious trick by the cucumber plant. The cunning cucumber keeps its cool and the beetles beat it.

Page 46: Strange seed stories quiz
Learning objective
To research for scientific purpose.
To draw conclusions based on evidence.

This quiz can be done in pairs or individually. Link it to the work you have done on seeds, encouraging the children to make sensible guesses and giving reasons for their answers. Invite them to set their own questions based on class work and research.

Page 47: The illustrated quiz
Learning objective
To present ideas clearly.
To draw conclusions based on evidence.

Focus your children on the illustrations in this quiz. Look carefully at what the artist has drawn and how he has presented this information. After completing the quiz, encourage your children to make their own illustrated quiz questions on a piece of folded card. Attach these to a bulletin board and ask the children to take it in turns to take down a question and attempt to solve it in a team situation, drawing their answers too, naturally!

Mix your own fertiliser answer:
b) d) e) These substances are rich in chemicals called minerals that plants need to grow strong and healthy. Actually, you need minerals too but you can get minerals from many types of food, so you don't have to eat blood and bones.

Vicious vegetable answers:
1 d)
2 a) This is a type of duckweed. Like any green plant, it makes food by photosynthesis and gives out oxygen as a by-product. The plants rise when they first produce this oxygen gas and sink after they get rid of it. The sight of all these plants bobbing up and down is a tourist attraction.
3 b) The prize exhibit is a 2000-year-old potato from Peru. Mind you, the potatoes used to make school dinners must be at least that old.
4 c) Chemical reactions in the leaves keep them a few degrees warmer than the surrounding soil and they can even melt snow.
5 e) Scientists aren't too sure why. The chemical (also used to preserve dead bodies) is drawn though holes in the plant's leaves and helps the roots grow longer.

Page 48: Ferocious and foul quiz
Learning objective
To research for scientific purpose.
To draw conclusions based on evidence.

Link this quiz to the work you have done on fruits and vegetables. Use the quiz as a springboard to encourage the children to do research either individually or in pairs and to decide for themselves what they want to find out, if appropriate.

NAME _____ DATE _____

Vicious vegetation!

Welcome to another world. This is a green and terrifying world where horrible things happen every day. A world where death is an ugly tendril slowly reaching out to strangle its victim. A world where there are no rules and the only aim is to stay alive. Welcome to the vicious world of veg.

Looks quiet, doesn't it? Maybe a little boring? Well, you couldn't be more wrong. Now take a closer look. Bigger plants are stealing light from smaller plants…

Trees are stealing light from everyone…   Plant roots are fighting for moisture…

My Vicious Veg observations list:

● Measure one square metre of ground.

● Look closely at everything you can find within your square.

● Make a list of your observations and draw the features you have found in your square.

NAME _____   DATE _____

POISONOUS PLANTS!

- Some plants can do us a lot of harm if we eat them.

- Use books and the internet to find out which ones are the very worst!

- Use this information to design your own poster warning younger children of the dangers.

HORRIBLE HEALTH WARNING!

Some plants are very poisonous and just nibbling a tiny corner of their leaves can give you a vicious stomachache. So sampling plants (even in the interests of science) is definitely out. (And don't test them on your little brother/sister/guinea pig or science teacher either.)

Picking plants is bad for their health. If it's rare you'll be putting it in extra danger. It's best to leave them where you find them.

DON'T!

DON'T!

Plan

Slogan:

Plants to avoid touching or eating:

Text and other information:

Drawings:

- Picking plants and flowers is not good for them! Design a logo to remind people not to do this.

NAME _____   DATE _____

Disgusting dissection

● If you look closely at plants you can discover just how amazing they are, outside and inside!

● You will need a magnifying glass and a pair of scissors as well as your green plant.

● Cut your plant using the scissors. Look closely at the newly opened surface, using your magnifying glass to get a better view.

● Compare what you see with the diagram on the right.

● Draw what you see in the box below, choosing your colours as accurately as possible.

What plants are made of
Look closely at a plant and you'll see it's made up of cells. These minute jelly-like objects make up all plants and animals. The sides of plant cells are strengthened with a substance called cellulose (cell-u-loze).

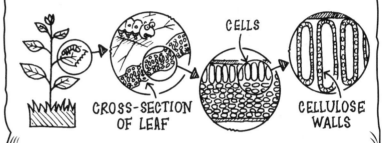

CROSS-SECTION OF LEAF   CELLS   CELLULOSE WALLS

Cellulose is the stuff that makes greens stringy. It makes up the roughage in your diet, which helps your body move your half-digested food through your guts. Most cellulose ends up in your poo. (Just in case you were wondering.)

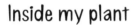

Inside my plant

● Write up your observations using these scientific headings:

Equipment (What we used)

Method (What we did)

Prediction (What I expected to see)

Result (What I saw)

Observations (My description)

NAME _____   DATE _____

Wonder Veg World!

- There are hundreds of thousands of different types of vegetable growing all over the world.

- Take a look at these vegetables on the right.

- Compare them to vegetables that you already know about, and make a list of the differences and similarities you have noticed.

- Now look at the class specimens of Wonder Veg that you have.

- Write a description of the outside, inside, smell and feel of these vegetables. Include drawings and comparisons with other vegetables that you know about.

The Wonder Veg Store
just in. . .
THE BRILLIANT BUFFALO GOURD
(Grows in Mexico and south-western USA)

- Huge 3-4 metre tubers.
- Weighs 30kg when two years old.
- Very tasty and rich in vegetable oils.
- Feeds the entire family.

a lot DELIVERY EXTRA!

THE WINGED BEAN
(It's a winged wonder)

A bean with wings. Don't like the sound of it? Don't scoff till you try it – you'll be eating your words. Yes, you really can eat the whole plant!

- Leaves taste like spinach.
- Flowers can be fried.
- Seed pods taste like green beans.
- Seeds taste like peas.
- Tubers cook like potatoes (and they're equally good for you).
- All this and it makes the soil full of nitrates thanks to bacteria in its roots. Wow!

THIS PRODUCT IS REALLY TAKING OFF

Our Wonder Veg!

_____

_____

_____

_____

_____

_____

_____

_____

_____

_____

_____

NAME _____   DATE _____

PLANTS: THE SECRET FACT FILE

● Plants are all around us, but we don't always know what they are up to!

● How many plants do you know?

● Make a list of as many as you can.

_____

_____

_____

_____

_____

_____

_____

NAME: Plants

THE BASIC FACTS: According to scientists, a plant is a living thing that makes its food from sunlight. Its leaves are usually green. If you break a plant's leaves colour rubs off on your hands. That's why some people say gardeners have green fingers. Ha ha!

THE VICIOUS DETAILS:

1 Some plants spice up their diet with dead insects. They catch the insects and then dissolve their bodies or suck out their insides.

2 Some plants happily feed on blood through their roots. (Dried blood is used in some fertilizers. It contains vital chemicals known as minerals that plants need.)

WOW! THAT PLANT'S GROWN QUICKLY!

● Draw and label your own plant file, adding as many vicious details as you can!

My Plant File

NAME _____   DATE _____

Attack of the killer plants!

- Plants have to be vicious at times – just to survive!

- Some guzzle insects even while the poor little creatures are alive and wriggling.

- They can be vicious to each other too – strangling their victims, sucking out their juices and stealing light!

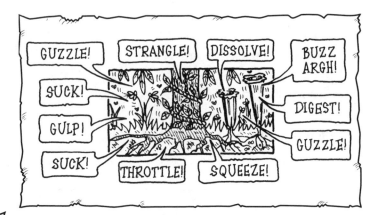

Dare you discover … how to make a plant attack you?

What you need:
A lot of bravery
A pea plant, a cucumber plant, a passion flower or any plant with tendrils
A pencil

What you do:
Gently stroke the tip of the tendril with the pencil.

What does the tendril do?
a) It grabs the pencil and snaps it in half.
b) The tendril draws back suddenly.
c) It slowly bends.

- What were the results of your experiment?

_____

_____

- Why do you think this happens?

_____

_____

- Imagine that you are the plant and have been arrested for attacking other plants growing nearby. Write your confession – including your motives – here.

My Confession

_____

_____

_____

_____

_____

NAME _____   DATE _____

Frightful fruity facts

Frightfully fruitful fruits

Can you tell the difference between a fruit and a vegetable? No – fruit *aren't* always sweeter than vegetables! Just think of a lemon! The difference between a fruit and a vegetable is that a vegetable can be any part of a plant – such as the root or the leaf. But a fruit has to form from a part of a flower called the ovary. (It's usually at the base of the flower.) Seeds form inside the fruit.

So let's ask a botanist to make things clear…

Well, the ovary was the bit in the flower that's at the base of the style. After the flower is pollinated the seeds start to form and the ovary swells up around them. Make sense so far? So to be a proper fruit and not just a common or garden vegetable, whatever you're eating had to have started off as the ovary of a flower.

● Can you guess which of the foods pictured below are fruit and which are veg? Draw a circle around the vegetables.

● Cut up these cards. Draw the foods and divide them into fruit and vegetables. Add your own cards, using the internet and books to help you.

Raspberry	Own choice	Own choice	Cabbage
Pumpkin	Garlic	Beetroot	Own choice
Own choice	Own choice	Apple	Cashew

NAME _____ DATE _____

FANTASTIC FOODS

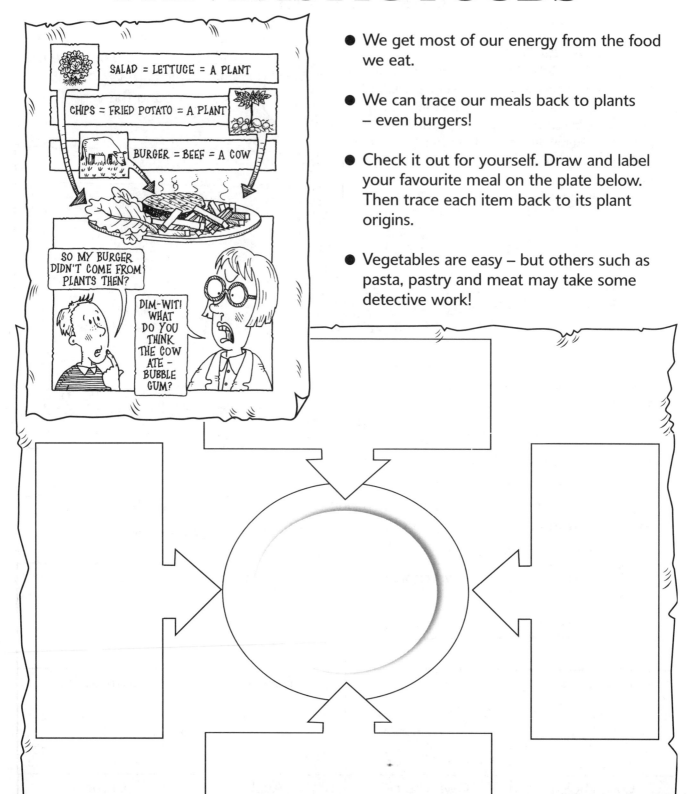

- We get most of our energy from the food we eat.

- We can trace our meals back to plants – even burgers!

- Check it out for yourself. Draw and label your favourite meal on the plate below. Then trace each item back to its plant origins.

- Vegetables are easy – but others such as pasta, pastry and meat may take some detective work!

- Draw a cartoon like the one at the top of this page to illustrate where your foods started out.

NAME _____ DATE _____

PESKY POLLEN 1

Dead horse arum
(Mediterranean islands)

PLAYS TRICKS ON: blow flies

LOW-DOWN DIRTY TRICKS:

1 Looks just like rotten meat. Makes a realistic stink so flies think they can lay their eggs inside it. Even provides a hole for them to explore what looks horribly like an empty eye socket.

2 Doesn't lay on food for the fly grubs when they hatch out. So they starve to death.

GET STUCK IN, KIDS

ROTTING MEAT STENCH

3 Traps the female flies in the flower until its stigmas pick up any pollen the flies might be carrying. Many flies die of suffocation inside the fiendish flower. (To be fair the flower does give them some nectar to drink.)

4 Flower only lets the flies out when they've been dusted with pollen. Ready to take to the next dead horse arum.

The mirror orchid
(Western Mediterranean)

PLAYS TRICKS ON: bees

LOW-DOWN DIRTY TRICKS:

1 The flower fools male bees into thinking it's a female bee. It looks like a female bee and even smells like one.

2 The male bee tries to give the flower a cuddle. The stamens swoop down and whack a blob of pollen on the male bee's head.

3 The bewildered bee flies off in search of another female, and usually ends up taking pollen to another mirror orchid.

YOO HOO!

I THINK I'M IN LOVE...

THWACK!

ERK!

POLLEN

YOU'LL NEVER GUESS WHAT JUST HAPPENED TO ME!

NAME: Pollination

THE BASIC FACTS: Pollination is how flowers make seeds. It's a straightforward job.

1 You make pollen in your flowers.

2 You transfer some of your pollen to another plant of your species. OK so far?

3 Then the other plant makes seeds that grow into baby plants. Easy-peasy.

THE VICIOUS DETAILS: All this pollen flying about can give people a stinking dose of hay fever.

HOW'S THE HAY FEVER?

DOT DOO BAD

● Take a look at your plant very closely.

● Draw and describe the pollen that you find, as well as where in the plant you found it.

My observations

NAME _____   DATE _____

Pesky pollen 2

- Plants breed when pollen from one plant reaches the stigmas of another.

- The pollen grows a tube in the second plant and seeds form.

- Now take a look at the pollen on your paintbrush and draw it here.

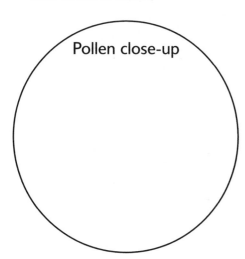

Pollen close-up

Dare you discover ... how to breed plants?
What you need:
A flower such as a daffodil or tulip
A small artist's paintbrush

What you do:
1 Lightly brush the anthers – these are the sticking-up bits on the stalks that are arranged in a circle in the centre of the flower.

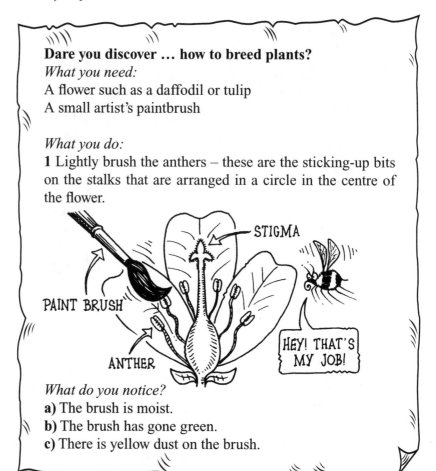

What do you notice?
a) The brush is moist.
b) The brush has gone green.
c) There is yellow dust on the brush.

- Use all your pollination information to draw a strip cartoon illustrating the process.

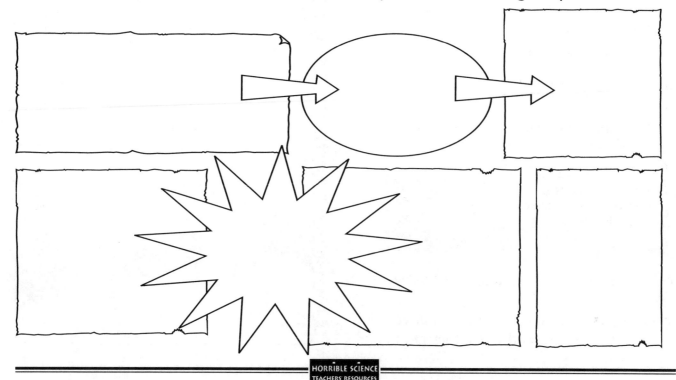

NAME _____   DATE _____

Starting seeds

- Once the plant is pollinated it can begin to grow a seed...

- Where are the seeds in the following foods?

  Cucumber   Avocado

  Apple   Tomato

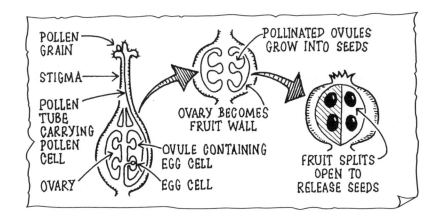

POLLEN GRAIN

STIGMA

POLLEN TUBE CARRYING POLLEN CELL

OVARY

OVULE CONTAINING EGG CELL

EGG CELL

POLLINATED OVULES GROW INTO SEEDS

OVARY BECOMES FRUIT WALL

FRUIT SPLITS OPEN TO RELEASE SEEDS

- With the help of an adult, cut the foods open. Draw and label them in your seed gallery below.

My seed gallery

NAME _____   DATE _____

SEED SECRETS

- A seed is like a space capsule filled with everything a plant needs to survive. Take this harmless little broad bean for example...

- This picture shows a germinated bean that has been (ha ha!) there a while. But how did it look before it reached this stage? And how will it look at the next stage?

- Open up your bean carefully and draw what you see. Some parts that may not seem important now will be useful later on.

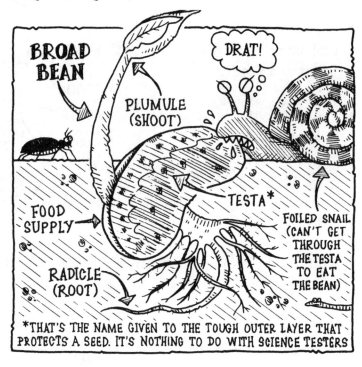

Inside the bean

- Now take another bean and plant it in your jam jar with damp cotton wool.

- Use the boxes below to help you keep a Bean Grower's Diary, drawing and describing the amazing changes that you will see.

3 days	1 week	10 days	2 weeks

NAME _____   DATE _____

Ripe or revolting?

● Some plants are clever enough to wrap their seeds in a tasty snack that can be eaten by animals and insects.

● Animals eat ripe fruits and carry the seeds with them in their bodies.

● Seeds pass through an animal's body and plop out some distance from the parent plant. This means the seedling has a good chance of finding more light and water to help it grow.

● But how do we know when fruit is ripe?

● Describe how your fruits smell and feel, inside and outside. Compare the ripe fruit to the unripe. Record your observations in the table below.

● How long do you think it will take each piece of unripe fruit to ripen? Make an estimate for each one and see how long it actually takes.

NAME: Fruits and seeds

THE BASIC FACTS: **1** Fruits and seeds are designed with one aim. To make sure the seedlings of a plant grow a distance away from the parent plant. That way they won't be fighting each other for light or water.

2 Seeds come in all shapes and sizes from orchid seeds that weigh 1 millionth of a gram to the 18 kg (40 lb) double coconut, which is also, amazingly, a seed.

THE VICIOUS DETAILS: Unripe fruits taste disgusting. That's the plant's way of making sure animals don't scoff the fruit before they're ripe. Some unripe fruit is even poisonous. Any animal that eats it will end up dead sorry. Well, mostly dead, actually.

P'RHAPS I'LL LEAVE THEM FOR A FEW MORE DAYS

| Fruit | Ripe | | Unripe | | Estimated time to ripen | Actual time taken to ripen |
	Smell	Feel	Smell	Feel		
Tomato						
Avocado						
Peach						

NAME _____   DATE _____

What's inside?

- Taking a look inside fruit can give us clues about what they are for.

- Not all of them are the same inside.

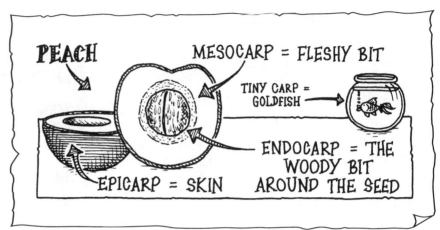

- Take a look at this collection. Draw and write your predictions of how they will look inside before discovering the facts! (Remember to label the skin, flesh and seeds.)

Fruit	Prediction	Result
Sugar snap peas		
Red pepper		
Tangerine		
Kiwi fruit		

- Add some of your own choices to the collection.

NAME _____ DATE _____

FOUL FERTILISERS

- Plants use fertilisers to help them grow.

- Gardeners add substances called fertilisers to the soil to help plants grow. Some of these substances are natural or organic. Others are chemicals made in factories.

- In the wild, the rotten remains of poo, plants and animals form a natural fertiliser.

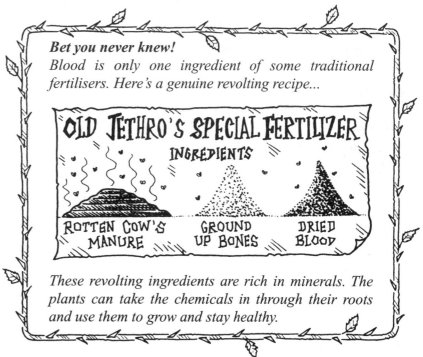

Bet you never knew!
Blood is only one ingredient of some traditional fertilisers. Here's a genuine revolting recipe...

OLD JETHRO'S SPECIAL FERTILIZER
INGREDIENTS

ROTTEN COW'S MANURE   GROUND UP BONES   DRIED BLOOD

These revolting ingredients are rich in minerals. The plants can take the chemicals in through their roots and use them to grow and stay healthy.

- Draw a line from the plant below to each of the things that you think would be a useful fertiliser.

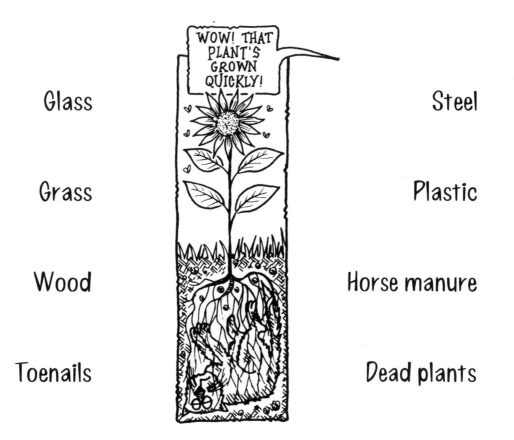

Glass

Grass

Wood

Toenails

WOW! THAT PLANT'S GROWN QUICKLY!

Steel

Plastic

Horse manure

Dead plants

- Add some ideas of your own and research them to see if you are right.

NAME _____   DATE _____

POO CORNER

- Poo smells disgusting but it's really useful for plants.

- Poo helps plants to grow because it's full of minerals. And when an animal's poo contains seeds, the poo forms a nice dollop of fresh fertiliser. Lovely!

- Take a look at this!

- Design an advert to promote the use of natural fertiliser and natural seed distribution through the use of... poo!

NAME _____ DATE _____

Victims of the Venus flytrap!

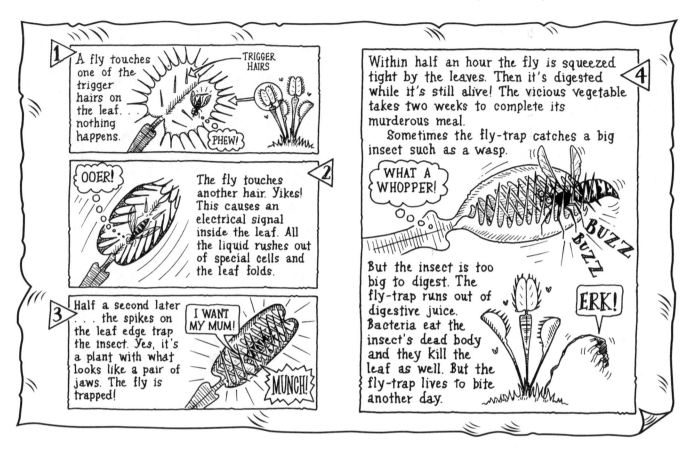

- Imagine that you are the fly! Write a fly's-eye account of your horrific ordeal. Remember to use the names of the plant parts as you warn your fellow flies of their frightening fate if they fall foul of the flytrap. Use the box below to plan your report.

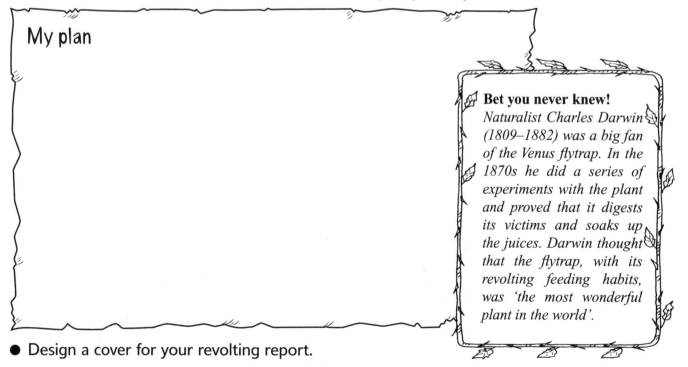

My plan

Bet you never knew!
Naturalist Charles Darwin (1809–1882) was a big fan of the Venus flytrap. In the 1870s he did a series of experiments with the plant and proved that it digests its victims and soaks up the juices. Darwin thought that the flytrap, with its revolting feeding habits, was 'the most wonderful plant in the world'.

- Design a cover for your revolting report.

NAME _____   DATE _____

Unusual suspects

- Take a look at your cactus. How would you identify it?

- Write a description here. Include information about colour, weight (including the pot) and height.

_____

_____

_____

_____

_____

_____

_____

THE ARIZONA GAZETTE

CROOKED CACTUS COWBOYS CAUGHT

The sheriff's office today reports that three cactus rustlers have been rounded up following a tip-off from a botanist. The rustlers, who were armed and dangerous, were taking cacti from the desert without a permit. Stolen cacti fetch huge prices from collectors in Europe and Japan but the ruthless rustlers are wiping these prickly plants out. They take huge numbers and cacti are getting scarce. And because these giant greens are so slow growing it will take ages before new cacti can grow and take their place. A botanist in the State Conservation Department said, "Cacti rustling sure is a prickly problem."

- Now look at your other plants. Draw and label them, comparing their colours, weights and heights.

Weight _____	Weight _____	Weight _____
Height _____	Height _____	Height _____
Plant 1	**Plant 2**	**Plant 3**

- Design a wanted poster so that people can identify and return your plants if they got rustled!

NAME _____   DATE _____

Fiendish flowers 1

Flowers – the inside story

1 The easiest way for a plant to spread pollen around is to let the wind blow it away. Plants such as grasses and willow trees grow big feathery stigmas to catch the pollen and dangle them out of their flowers.

2 Most flowering plants use animals to take their pollen from one plant to another. But first they need to grab the animal's attention. And for this they need PUBLICITY. Yes, we're talking about razzmatazz – flowers, colours, perfumes – the works!

3 Next they need sticky nectar to feed the animals.

I mean, they're not going to shift pollen out of the goodness of their little hearts, are they?

4 Plants employ a surprising range of creatures. There are flies, beetles, hummingbirds, bats – yes, bats. (Some tropical flowers open at night so bats can pollinate them.)

5 To show how it actually works we took this cute little flower…

and hacked it in half…

● What do you think it will look like inside? Draw your prediction here.

● How do underwater plants breed? Use books and the internet to help you find out.

NAME _____ DATE _____

Fiendish flowers 2

● This flower has been carefully dissected. Now we can see inside. The artist has drawn and labelled it very clearly.

● Take a look at your collection of flowers. Handle them carefully so that you can find the stamen, stigma, style and ovary in each of them. Draw and label what you see.

My flower drawings

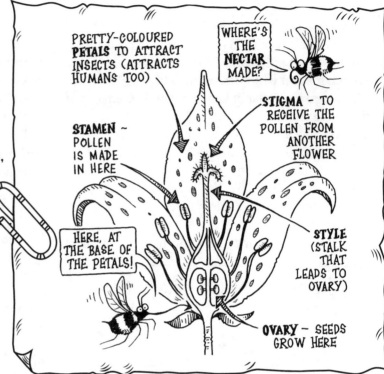

PRETTY-COLOURED **PETALS** TO ATTRACT INSECTS (ATTRACTS HUMANS TOO)

WHERE'S THE **NECTAR** MADE?

STAMEN ~ POLLEN IS MADE IN HERE

STIGMA - TO RECEIVE THE POLLEN FROM ANOTHER FLOWER

HERE, AT THE BASE OF THE PETALS!

STYLE (STALK THAT LEADS TO OVARY)

OVARY ~ SEEDS GROW HERE

BOTANIST
~~NAME~~ _____   DATE _____

BRUTAL BUG-EATERS 1

● All these plants are real. They eat bugs! Look closely at how they are designed.

The waterwheel plant
Found in Europe, Australia and Africa.
The waterwheel plant lives in ponds and eats tiny pond creatures.

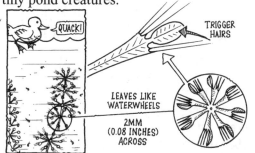

TRIGGER HAIRS

LEAVES LIKE WATERWHEELS

2MM (0.08 INCHES) ACROSS

And here's what happens...

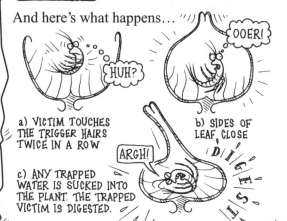

OOER!

HUH?

a) VICTIM TOUCHES THE TRIGGER HAIRS TWICE IN A ROW

b) SIDES OF LEAF CLOSE

ARGH!

DIGEST!

c) ANY TRAPPED WATER IS SUCKED INTO THE PLANT. THE TRAPPED VICTIM IS DIGESTED.

The pitcher plant
Found in the USA, South America and Australia.

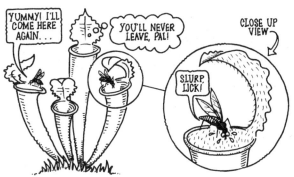

YUMMY! I'LL COME HERE AGAIN...

YOU'LL NEVER LEAVE, PAL!

CLOSE UP VIEW

SLURP LICK!

Here's an X-ray view so you can see what's going on inside...

X-RAY PICTURE OF A PITCHER!

WAXY, FLAKY SURFACE. IT'S SLIPPERY AS SOAP. THERE'S NO ESCAPE NOW.

DOWNWARD POINTING HAIRS MAKE IT EVEN MORE SLIPPERY

ARGH!

VICTIM FALLS INTO THE POOL OF WATER AND IT'S NOT A NICE LITTLE SWIMMING POOL EITHER.

DIGESTIVE GLANDS SQUIRT OUT ACID TO DISSOLVE THE VICTIM

The sundew plant
Found all over the world from Australia to the USA. A sundew plant works like this...

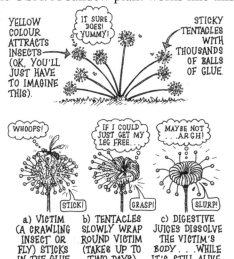

YELLOW COLOUR ATTRACTS INSECTS (OK, YOU'LL JUST HAVE TO IMAGINE THIS).

IT SURE DOES! YUMMY!

STICKY TENTACLES WITH THOUSANDS OF BALLS OF GLUE.

WHOOPS!

IF I COULD JUST GET MY LEG FREE...

MAYBE NOT ...ARGH!

STICK!

GRASP!

SLURP!

a) VICTIM (A CRAWLING INSECT OR FLY) STICKS IN THE GLUE

b) TENTACLES SLOWLY WRAP ROUND VICTIM (TAKES UP TO TWO DAYS)

c) DIGESTIVE JUICES DISSOLVE THE VICTIM'S BODY...WHILE IT'S STILL ALIVE.

● Design your own bug-eating plant.

● Write down some of your ideas here. Think about the types of bugs it will eat and how it could digest them.

_____

_____

_____

_____

_____

_____

_____

BOTANIST
~~NAME~~ _____   DATE _____

Brutal bug-eaters 2

Name of my plant:

_____

My plant attracts:

_____

It does this by:

_____

It traps the bug by:

_____

It digests the bug by:

_____

NAME: Bug-eating plants

THE BASIC FACTS: In some swampy areas there aren't enough minerals to feed plants. The soil is especially low in the nitrates that plants need to grow. Plants help themselves to extra nitrates by scoffing insects.

HAVE YOU GOT ANTS IN YOUR PANTS?

NO. I'VE GOT BUGS IN MY PETTICOATS!

THE VICIOUS DETAILS: Some bug-eating plants look pretty. The Australian pink petticoat plant looks like a tiny pink petticoat. (How sweet!) But an unwary bug that crawls inside finds itself in a trap and is digested . . . alive.

My bug-eating plant

BEWARE!

NAME _____   DATE _____

POWERFUL PLANTS

For thousands of years people have used plants as medicines. But how would you get on as a traditional plant doctor? Can you match the plant to its medical effects?

Plants to choose from:
1 South American cinchona tree bark

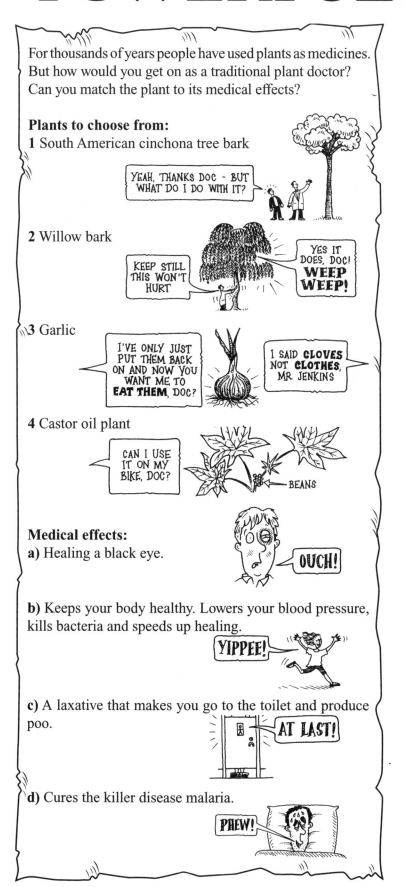

YEAH, THANKS DOC – BUT WHAT DO I DO WITH IT?

2 Willow bark

KEEP STILL THIS WON'T HURT

YES IT DOES, DOC! **WEEP WEEP!**

3 Garlic

I'VE ONLY JUST PUT THEM BACK ON AND NOW YOU WANT ME TO **EAT THEM**, DOC?

I SAID **CLOVES** NOT **CLOTHES**, MR JENKINS

4 Castor oil plant

CAN I USE IT ON MY BIKE, DOC?

— BEANS

Medical effects:
a) Healing a black eye.

OUCH!

b) Keeps your body healthy. Lowers your blood pressure, kills bacteria and speeds up healing.

YIPPEE!

c) A laxative that makes you go to the toilet and produce poo.

AT LAST!

d) Cures the killer disease malaria.

PHEW!

BEAN HAS BEEN

Answers:

1 d) The bark of the South American cinchona tree contains a drug called quinine. This kills microscopic creatures that cause the deadly disease malaria. Unfortunately, taking the bark kills the tree. But people were so desperate for treatment that in the nineteenth century thousands of trees had to die.

2 a) Willow bark contains a chemical called salicylic acid. It's roughly the same chemical as the painkiller aspirin. This explains why country people used to put strips of willow bark over a black eye. But the wily willow isn't making aspirin for us. Oh no – it's there to kill off hungry beetles. Yes, beetles soon discover that they're barking up the wrong tree. Ha ha.

3 b) Yep – these are official facts. Scientific tests have proved that chewing garlic is good for you. And as long as you've got your health, who needs friends?

4 c) Castor oil is a laxative. It was typically used to torture children. However, castor oil has a sinister secret. It has to be prepared carefully because the castor oil bean contains a poison so deadly that one bean can kill a person.

● How did you do?

● Add some Powerful Plants facts of your own and try them on your partner.

NAME _____   DATE _____

Foul fungi

If plants are vicious, fungi are – well, super vicious. In fact, the only people who like fungi are gourmets who like to eat them and botanists who like to study them.

HAVE YOU FINISHED WITH IT YET? I'M STARVING!

So what do you think? Are fungi really that bad? Well, yes, they are.

Dare you discover … how to grow your own fungi?

What you need:
A slice of white bread
A little water
A clear polythene bag

What you do:
1 Sprinkle a little water on the bread so it's slightly moist
2 Place the bread in the bag and seal it tightly.
3 Leave the bread in a warm place for 2–3 days.

What do you notice?
If you're lucky you should find some grey-green fungi growing on the bread. Where do you think it came from?
a) The bread
b) The bag
c) The air in the bag

● Read the Fungi Fact File to find out why...

NAME: Fungi

THE BASIC FACTS: **1** Fungi aren't real plants. They have no stems, no roots and they don't make food by photosynthesis.

2 Unlike plants they don't contain cellulose (that's the stuff in roughage, remember). Instead, they are made up of chitin (kitin). By some weird coincidence this is also the chemical that makes up insects' jaws.

THE VICIOUS DETAILS: Fungi feed by:

🍄 Sticking feeding tubes called hyphae into their food.

🍄 Making an acid that dissolves the food.

🍄 Sucking up the juices. Sometimes the "food" is a living plant or animal.
Some plants fight back. If they sense the acid, they grow extra thick roots or leaves so the hyphae can't break in.

ARGH! LEAF' ME ALONE!

THE CLEVER THING'S TO BE THICK!

SUCK!   SLURP!

● Draw and describe what you see after:

10 minutes	2 days	5 days	2 weeks

NAME _____   DATE _____

Fab photosynthesis 2 – Rambling roots

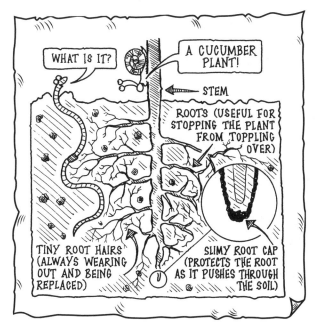

- Photosynthesis is the way plants make food.

- After taking in sunlight and carbon dioxide through their leaves, the second step is to suck up water and minerals through hairs on their roots.

- Take a look at the roots of these plants and draw them.
  Cress   Grass   Broad Bean   Spider plant

- What similarities and differences do you notice?

- Take two spider plants and remove the roots from one. Plant them in the same sized pots and water them. Put them in a sunny window and don't let them dry out or become water logged. Draw what happens to each of them.

	Newly planted	After 1 day	After 1 week	After 2 weeks
Plant 1				
Plant 2 (no roots)	Newly planted	After 1 day	After 1 week	After 2 weeks

- What do you think this test was designed to find out?

- Was the test fair or unfair? Give a reason for your answer.

NAME _____ DATE _____

Fab photosynthesis 3 — Simply starch

● After taking in sunlight and carbon dioxide through their leaves and sucking up water through their roots, plants then use them them to make their food.

● They use sunlight to make a tiny electrical current and split water into hydrogen and oxygen. The hydrogen is combined with carbon dioxide to make a type of sugar.

● The sugars are stored as another chemical called starch.

● But how do we know that they are really all doing this and not just ordering their food off a menu?

● Cover a leaf on a green tree or bush with a piece of card so that it covers both sides. Use paper clips to keep it in place.

● Leave it for a week during some sunny days and then uncover the leaf and take it off the tree or bush. What do you think will happen?

● Compare it to the others on the tree.

Covered leaf   Uncovered leaf

● Now challenge your teacher to do the Simply Starch test to see how much starch the leaves have produced. Write it up using these headings: equipment, method, prediction, results and conclusion. Include diagrams to help illustrate what happened.

● Were the tests fair? Explain your reasons for your answer.

_____

_____

NAME _____   DATE _____

Terrific transpiration

IT'S TRANSPIRATION!

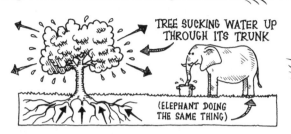

TREE SUCKING WATER UP THROUGH ITS TRUNK

(ELEPHANT DOING THE SAME THING)

Shouldn't that be perspiration?

No, she's talking about her plant. Transpiration is when plants soak up water through their roots and lose it through the stomata in their leaves. This ensures a stream of water to their leaves for photosynthesis. It's a bit like you slurping a drink through a really long straw.

Plants lose huge amounts of water through transpiration. An average-sized lawn – 15.2 x 6 metres – can lose 50 tons of water every year and a large tree can lose 1,000 litres in a single sunny day. No wonder plants get thirsty.

Dare you discover … transpiration?

What you need:
A plant
A polythene bag
An elastic band

What you do:
1 Cover a branch and a few leaves with the polythene bag.
2 Secure the edges of the bag with the elastic band so that air can't get into the bag.
3 Leave it in a sunny place for four hours.

What do you notice?
a) The bag has been sucked in.
b) The bag has been blown outwards.
c) The inside of the bag is covered with tiny water droplets.

● What do you think will happen? Write a sentence explaining why you think this.

_____

_____

● Draw a strip cartoon illustrating what happened in the right order.

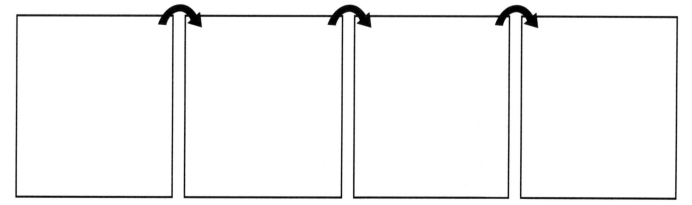

NAME _____   DATE _____

LUSCIOUS LEAVES

● Leaves are very important as they help plants breathe and feed.

● They come in many different shapes and sizes.

● Collect your leaves together and compare them. What differences and similarities do you notice?

● Do your leaf rubbings in the box below.

● Can you feel any bumps and ridges when you are rubbing? What do you think they may be caused by?

NAME: Leaves

THE BASIC FACTS: 1 Leaves are the green part on a plant. They're normally found at the end of stalks.

2 If you look at a leaf closely you'll see a maze of tiny tubes. They're for carrying water and carting away sugars made by photosynthesis.

THE VICIOUS DETAILS: Plants such as the piggyback plant can grow a whole new body from just one leaf. Imagine your finger falling off. And then your whole body re-growing from your finger. That's what plants can do!

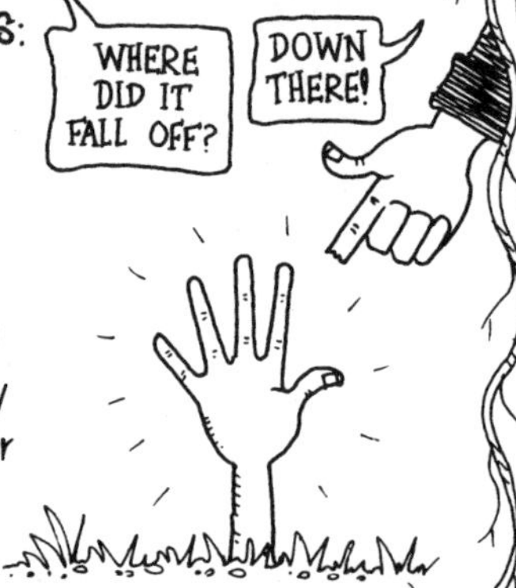

WHERE DID IT FALL OFF?

DOWN THERE!

My leaf rubbings

● Make a collection of full-colour leaf rubbings and compare leaves of outdoor and indoor plants. Use books and the internet to help compile a class Book of Luscious Leaves.

Amazing leaf facts

1 The leaves of the sensitive plant are surprisingly… sensitive. If you touch them the stem bows down to the ground and the plant folds into a spike. This puts off most hungry animals – well, it would, wouldn't it? Have you ever had a salad that tried to escape?

2 What happens is that the touch triggers an electrical current inside the leaf. This empties all the liquid out of cells in the base of the leaves and makes them collapse. So remember this plant is sensitive and don't go upsetting it by saying cruel things like 'vinaigrette dressing'.

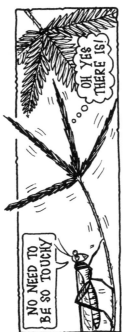

NO NEED TO BE SO TOUCHY

OH YES THERE IS!

3 Some of the biggest leaves belong to a species of arum plant. Its huge leaves are 3 metres wide. Some travellers use them as tents but you can also eat them. (Note: It's a bad idea to nibble holes in your tent.)

4 Talking about huge leaves – Amazon water lily leaves are 2 metres across. They're so strong that the first gardener to grow them, Joseph Paxton (1801–1865), dressed his daughter as a fairy and photographed her sitting on a leaf.

Bet she felt a right idiot. (This won't work with normal-sized water lilies.)

CHILD SITTING ON GIANT AMAZON WATER LILY

CHILD SITTING ON NORMAL WATER LILY

G.L.U.G...!

5 Ever wondered why leaves turn pretty colours and fall in autumn? Well, amazingly, the leaves are pushed out by the tree! In cold countries it's tough for trees in the winter. They find it hard to suck up water from the cold soil. It's a bit like you trying to suck ice cream through a straw. So the trees shut up shop. There's no use keeping those useless water-losing leaves.

6 Those pretty colours come from leftover and unwanted chemicals in the leaves. The valuable green chlorophyll gets sucked back into the tree whilst more waste chemicals pour into the leaf.

7 And when the leaf falls it's like the tree is going to the toilet – or should that be lav-a-tree? The tree makes chemicals that loosen the stalk from the branch. So it flutters gently down to earth.

● Some of these amazing facts have excellent cartoons to illustrate them. The artist has left some for you to do. Cut out the facts that need cartoons and design your own to add to your Book of Luscious Leaves.

NAME _____   DATE _____

Stunning stems

- Here is an x-ray view of a cucumber plant's stem.

- Once a plant's roots have sucked up water and minerals it is the stem's job to take them to the leaves for photosynthesis to start. It uses tubes called xylem (you say it 'zy-lem').

- The sugar made by photosynthesis moves around other tubes in the stem, called phloem (pronounced 'flow-em').

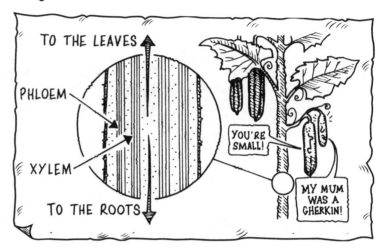

- But the best way to see a stem's stunning suckering skills is... to prove it!

You will need: White carnation; jam jar; water; blue food colouring.

Method: Fill the jar half full of water and add some food colouring. Put the white carnation into the jar.

Prediction: What do you think will happen?

_____

Results: Draw and describe what you see.

Start	1 hour	3 hours	1 day	2 days

- What happened to the carnation? Why do you think this is?

_____

NAME _____   DATE _____

Vital vegetables quiz

Priceless plant products
Can you match the
following plants with the
products they make?

Plants to choose from:
1 Sugar cane
2 Stinging nettles
3 Seaweed
4 Wheat
5 Lichen
6 The South American
bixa tree
7 Cotton
8 Rubber
9 Pine trees

● Draw the plants on
these cards.

**Products to choose
from:**
a) A pair of very smelly
socks
b) Fuel for cars
c) A nice plate of
spaghetti
d) Dye
e) A dirty old wellie boot
(where's the other one got
to?)
f) Forecasting the weather
g) A tablecloth
h) Lovely orange hair
i) A book

● Draw the products on
these cards.

● Cut out the cards and put them into two piles. Pick one from the plants and try and match
it with the product it makes. Add some of your own and play with a partner.

Jungle of Death quiz 1

Just imagine you're a plant. So you thought plants have it easy just sitting around in the soil all day, waiting for the rain to rain and the sun to shine. You thought they didn't have to worry about a thing? Well, get this. Life in the plant world is one battle after another, and plants have to use some pretty vicious tricks to stay alive.

OK, now here's your chance to put yourself in a plant's position and see if *you* can survive. But beware – you'll have to fight for your life! You could see savage snails, insect invaders and crafty caterpillars. Are you ready? Remember, there's no peeping at the answers and no going back! **Will you survive THE JUNGLE OF DEATH?**

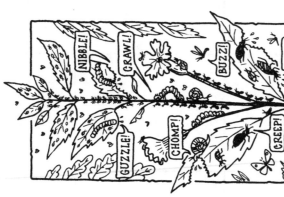

NIBBLE! CRAWL! BUZZ! CHEW! GUZZLE! CHOMP! CREEP! MUNCH! RASP!

HOPE THERE'S SOME LEFT WHEN WE GET THERE!

● Cut out these questions for your quiz.

RASP! RASP! RASP! RASP! RASP!

1 Watch out! There's a huge savage slimy snail rasping its jaws on the underside of your leaves. What do you do?

a) Make slippery slime under the leaves. The snails would slide off your leaves.

b) Grow spikes on the undersides of your leaves to neatly kebab the snail.

c) Allow the snails to feed. Don't panic! The snails will never eat all your leaves and what's left will grow again.

2 Cut-throat caterpillars are crunching your leaves. If you don't stop them they'll eat you alive. What's your plan?

a) Drop off the affected leaves – that'll take the caterpillars with them. And good riddance!

b) Grow extra-thick leaves. The leaves would be too thick and chewy for the caterpillars to bite through.

c) Make a gas. It's an SOS signal to passing wasps.

3 You're surrounded! On every side there are insects that want to eat your leaves. You've got to raise your own army to fight them off. Which are the best creatures to use? Better decide right now!

a) Ants – good for attack.

b) Woodlice – good for defence.

c) Rats – bigger than insects.

Jungle of Death quiz 2

4 Action stations – DANGER! A vicious half-starved rabbit is attacking your leaves! How can you fight it off?
a) Quickly grow a tendril. The wind will make the tendril wave around. This will frighten off the furry monster.
b) Open your flowers suddenly to scare it away.
c) Hit back. Sting the rabbit on the nose.

5 You've got time to think about this one. Some bugs have laid their eggs on you. These eggs are like little ticking time bombs. In the spring the eggs will hatch and the bugs will start stuffing themselves on your tender spring leaves. What's your plan?
a) Don't produce any new leaves in the spring.
b) Produce new leaves unexpectedly early or unexpectedly late so the bugs don't know when to hatch.
c) Make poisons in the new leaves.

ARGHHH! I DON'T BELIEVE IT!

WHAT'S HAPPENING OUT THERE?

IS IT a), b), OR c)?

BUG EGGS

6 Danger from the air! They're landing. An army of aphids. They've come to suck juices from your leaves. You've only got minutes to fight back. Quick, what will you do?
a) Send extra juices to your outer leaves so the aphids go and feed there. Then set up an ambush.

b) Send extra juices to the leaves where the aphids are feeding. The aphids will drink until they swell up and go pop. It's messy but deadly.
c) Pump the juices out of your leaves. The aphids will go away because they will have nothing to feed on. That's right, starve them into surrender.

MESSAGE TO ALL LEAVES...
APHID ATTACK!

ARGH!

7 More insect invaders are marching up your stem. This time they're beetles and they mean business. They're biting your leaves to pieces. You've got to act now . . . or DIE!
a) Try to fold up your leaves so the beetles get trapped inside.
b) Pump water out of the tiny holes in your leaves and try to wash the beetles away.
c) Make a gas that smells like a female beetle. If they're males they'll try and find the female and leave you in peace.

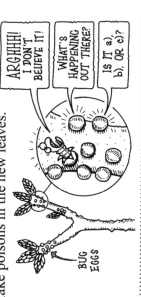

BET I CAN 'BEAT ALL' OF YOU TO THE TOP

● Use your Horrible Science knowledge to add some questions of your own!

NAME _____ DATE _____

Strange seed stories quiz

● Can you tell whether these strange seed stories are true or false?

1 As the Mediterranean squirting cucumber ripens it makes more and more slimy juice until it explodes.

2 The sharp hooks of the grapple plant seeds stick into an elephant's foot. They only fall off after the hook has been worn out by being walked on for quite a distance. For the elephant this vicious plant is a jumbo-sized problem.

3 But elephants actually help protect acacia tree seeds from beetles by eating the seeds.

4 Deadly nightshade berries kill the animal that eats them and the vicious seedling grows out of the dead animal's body.

5 Australian mistletoe seeds are spread by a bird wiping its bum on a tree.

6 The South American hura tree is known as the monkey's dinner bell because of its bell-shaped

DO YOU MIND!

seeds. Monkeys love to eat them for dinner.

7 Mangrove seeds fall downwards like spears. (That's why it's not a good idea to have a kip under a mangrove tree.)

THEY HANG DOWN... | LIKE GREEN SPEARS. | I JUST DON'T SEE... | THE POINT OF IT - UGH!

● Now add some true or false questions of your own.

Answers:

1 TRUE. It splatters slimy juice and seeds everywhere. Guaranteed to liven up any school dinner.

2 TRUE. Then the seeds germinate and the elephant is left hopping mad.

3 TRUE. Beetles break into the pods and seed capsules and guzzle the seeds. If an elephant eats the pods the seeds survive but the beetles get digested.

4 FALSE.

5 TRUE. Australian mistletoe is a plant that grows on trees. It makes very sticky berries. The mistletoe bird eats the berries and gets rid of the seeds in their poo. But the seeds are also sticky – and they get glued to the bird's bum. So the bird wipes its bum on a tree (no – they don't use toilet paper). The seed sticks to the tree and that's just where the seedling wants to grow. You might like to explain these disgusting details when someone you don't like wants to kiss you under the mistletoe at Christmas.

6 FALSE. The name comes from the popping noise made by the seed cases as they dry up and pop open to scatter the seeds. Which is odd because the sound is like pistol shots and often scares travellers. And it's nothing like a dinner bell.

7 TRUE. Mangrove trees grow on muddy shorelines. The seeds are joined to green spikes and germinate on the tree. Then the spikes fall into the mud below. Roots quickly anchor the spike in the mud and a new tree starts to grow. If the tide is in, the spike floats away like a little boat for an exciting ocean cruise – in search of a new place to grow.

The illustrated quiz

Gruesome greenery

A plant is a living thing (usually green) that can use sunlight to transform carbon dioxide gas in the air into food – a trick called photosynthesis (fo-toe-sinth-e-sis). Bug-eating plants also eat insects, and as for the rest, well, a nice drop of blood makes a lovely treat...

Mix your own fertiliser quiz

Choose THREE of the ingredients below to make a traditional fertiliser.

a) WOOD SHAVINGS

b) GROUND-UP BONES (NOT HUMAN).

c) EGG WHITE

d) BLOOD (THE DRIED VARIETY IS FINE).

e) ROTTING HORSE OR COW POO (ANYONE FANCY MUCKING OUT THE FARMYARD?)

f) OLD TOENAILS

g) CHALK

Vicious vegetable quiz

All you have to do in this quiz is match the question to its correct answer.

QUESTIONS

1 If you stretched out all the plant roots in a tennis-court-sized garden they would cover twice the distance to...?

2 What makes people stand on the banks of Lake Akan in Japan and stare at the water?

3 Where is the world's only potato museum?

4 How did the Feverish Skunk Cabbage get its name?

5 What helps spider plants grow strong and healthy?

ANSWERS

b) BLACKFOOT, IDAHO.

d) THE MOON.

a) PLANTS THAT DIVE UP AND DOWN IN THE WATER.

c) THE PLANT IS WARMER THAN ITS SURROUNDINGS.

e) THEY ENJOY A FEW PUFFS OF FORMALIN.

● This quiz has lots of good illustrations. Make up some of your own illustrated quiz questions and try them on your partner.

Ferocious and foul quiz

Ferocious flowers and foul fruits quiz answers (total score eight points):

1 b) The Australian mistletoe bird eats the seeds and they come out in its poo. The bird then wipes its bum on a tree and the seed can grow on the tree.

2 a) The rafflesia is also known as the 'stinking corpse lily'. It rots into a black stinking mass and makes a lovely Christmas gift for your teacher.

3 h) Bananas DON'T grow on trees. Bananas are giant plants and the banana fruits are specially bred without seeds so they can be eaten easily. (The black bits inside a banana are the traces of where the seeds should be.)

4 c) Freshwater lakes in many parts of the world are being taken over and choked by the horrible hyacinths.

5 g) Loofahs are a tropical fruit rather like a marrow. The fruit has been dried out to make it hard and scratchy. In the Second World War the fibres in the fruit were used to make padding for helmets.

6 f) Evening primrose flowers are closed in the day and open at dusk. Evening primrose oil is used to treat the skin disease eczema.

7 d) The spooky thing is that every one of these bamboo plants wherever they are on Earth will flower and die at the same moment.

8 e) It's guaranteed to liven up a school dinner.

Ferocious flowers and foul fruits quiz

All you have to do is match the plant to the fact. (By the way, these plants may sound putrid but they really exist!)

Plants

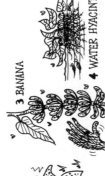

1 A TYPE OF AUSTRALIAN MISTLETOE

2 RAFFLESIA

3 BANANA

4 WATER HYACINTH

5 LOOFAH

6 EVENING PRIMROSE

7 PHYLLOSTACHYS (STA-CKIS-TO-STACKYS)

8 MEDITERRANEAN SQUIRTING CUCUMBER BAMBOO

Facts

a) It pongs of rotting flesh and attracts flies.

b) This plant grows on trees. It has sticky seeds that stick to a bird's bum.

c) A disaster for lakes. One plant can breed 60,000 more in a few months.

d) It flowers every 120 years.

e) It might splatter you with green slime.

f) Its flowers pop out for the evening.

g) People use this fruit to scratch their backs in the bath.

h) This seedless fruit doesn't grow on trees.

• Use the internet and books to help you research extra questions for the most horrible Horrible Science Quiz ever!